Little Chimp and the Termites

Story by Beverley Randell
Illustrations by Rachel Tonkin

One day, Mother Chimp
went into the forest
with Baby Chimp.

Little Chimp ran along, too.
He saw a brown hill
and he stopped to look at it.

Mother Chimp said,
"There are a lot of termites
inside that brown hill.
I'm going to catch some."

Mother Chimp
went to find a stick.
"Look at this,"
she said to Little Chimp.

They went back
to the brown hill.
Little Chimp saw
some tiny holes
in the hill.

Mother Chimp put the stick into one of the holes.

She put it down a tunnel.

Mother Chimp sat very still.

"I will take my stick out now," said Mother Chimp. "Look!"

She had five termites on her stick.
"Here you are," she said.

Little Chimp put a termite into his mouth.

It was very good to eat.

Now Little Chimp
wanted to catch
some termites, too.
He ran to find a stick.

Little Chimp came back
to the termite hill
with his little stick.
He put it
into one of the tiny holes.

He sat very still.

"I will take my stick out now,"
he said.

Little Chimp

looked at his stick.

There were **no** termites on it.

"That hole was no good,"

said Little Chimp.

"I will find a new one."

He put his stick
into a new hole.

And **this** time,
clever Little Chimp
got some termites to eat.